THE TWO BROTHERS

Quran Stories for Little Hearts

SANIYASNAIN KHAN

Designed and Illustrated by
Achla Anand & Achal K. Anand

First published 2001
Reprinted, 2002
© Goodword Books 2002

www.goodwordforkids.com

Goodword Books
1, Nizamuddin West Market
New Delhi-110 013
Tel. 435 6666, 435 5454, 435 1128
Fax 9111-435 7333, 435 7980
e-mail: info@goodwordbooks.com

THE RIGHT STEP

Long long ago, when Allah created the beautiful world,
He decided to create a human being, so he created the first man,
Adam ﷺ. Allah also created the first woman, Hawwa (Eve), as a helper
and loving companion to Adam ﷺ. The Prophet Adam ﷺ and his wife
happily began their lives on the earth.

2

Imagine what the earth would have been like at that time. When there were no human beings apart from them. No pollution, no noise, no crowds... There was peace and great harmony everywhere.

4

The Prophet Adam ﷺ and Hawwa were blessed with two sons, Habil (Abel) and Qabil (Cain). When they grew up, Habil, the younger brother, became a shepherd. He herded sheep, goats and other animals.

The elder brother, Qabil, worked as a farmer, tilling the fields.

One day both decided to make a sacrifice to please their Lord. Habil took the best of his flock, while Qabil brought his crops. They usually laid out the sacrifice in a high place. If a fire came down from heaven and burnt the offering to ashes, it was a sign that Allah was pleased with it.

Suddenly a spark of light flashed and burnt Habil's offering to ashes. This showed that Allah accepted his sacrifice, but rejected Qabil's sacrifice. Qabil's failure made him hate and feel jealous of his younger brother. He felt it was Habil's fault that he was put to shame. Habil tried to explain to Qabil why his sacrifice had not been accepted: "In your heart you have no fear of Allah," Habil said to his brother. "That is why Allah did not accept your sacrifice."

But, instead of agreeing and feeling sorry for his mistake, Qabil felt hurt at being disgraced and insulted. His face darkened with anger and his heart became hardened: "No," cried Qabil, "I will kill you!"

At this threat from his elder brother, Habil did not shout back. He just said calmly: "Even if you raise your hand to kill me, I will not fight back, for I fear Allah, the Lord of the Worlds." These fine words spoken by his younger brother could not calm Qabil, as he was blinded by jealousy and puffed up with arrogance and anger. Qabil's anger got the better of him and he killed his innocent brother Habil.

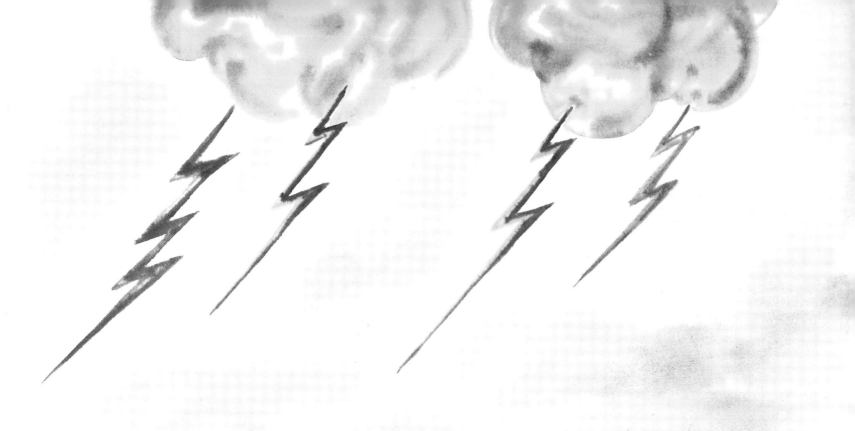

But no sooner had he done this horrifying deed than he began to change. Seeing the blood spilled all around the motionless body of his younger brother, Qabil's anger slowly cooled. Now he realized what a big mistake he had made. He had acted in haste, he had done something vile, and now, thinking about it, he felt very sorry.

For hours he sat nearby, shamed and grief-stricken, looking down at his brother's mute, blood-spattered body: "Now I have killed my brother," said Qabil to himself in deep sorrow, "but what shall I do with his body?"

Then Allah sent a raven, which landed on the ground near the body. The raven began to scratch the ground to tell Qabil that he should bury his brother's dead body under the earth.

"Woe is me!" cried Qabil helplessly. "I am worse even than this raven, for I cannot hide my brother's corpse." Qabil felt his meanness all the more so, because even a raven could teach him a lesson.

The moral of this story is that two believers should never fight with each other. Even if one of them is bent on fighting, the other one, like the obedient Habil, should never fight back. The Quran says: "If anyone killed a person—except as punishment for murder or other corruption in the land—it shall be looked upon as if he had killed all mankind. And whoever saved a human life, shall be looked upon as if he had saved all mankind." (*Surah al-Maidah*, 5:32)

Alayhis Salam
'May peace be upon him.'
The customary blessings on the prophets.